This Book
Belongs to:

_____

Forward

Hello everybody! Welcome to the Traveling Bear Journeys.

The Journey, *Traveling Bear Skis Gold Mountain*, emphasizes the power of positive thinking. Read this journey with your child. At the end, complete the "What's Most Important?" exercise with your child. The purpose of this exercise is to help your child recognize the positive behavioral patterns that are exemplified throughout the journey and motivate your child to go after something special.

Remember, have fun and just find a way to get there!

Visit Traveling Bear at www.travelingbear.com

Traveling Bear™
SKis Gold Mountain

"Thinking Positively"

Traveling Bear, Chuga, and Mookie went skiing for the day.

"We're going to ski down big Gold Mountain," said Traveling Bear.

Chuga looked nervous. "I think I'll stick with the beginners' slope," he said with a gulp.

"Don't be silly," said Mookie. "You've skied down this mountain lots of times. You can do this, Chuga. Think positively!"

"I can do this," whispered Chuga. "I can do this. I CAN DO THIS!"

The three friends took the lift up to the top of Gold Mountain.

"How come we stopped?" asked Mookie.

"I don't know," said Traveling Bear. "But let's think really hard that in five seconds, we'll get going again!"

"Okay," said Mookie. "Let's count!"

"One, two, three, four, five," said Chuga, closing his eyes really tight. "Are we moving yet?"

"Yes!" cried Traveling Bear. "We are moving! Positive thinking really works!"

Everyone had a great run down the mountain.

"Let's do it again!" said Traveling Bear.

"Wait," said Chuga. "I need some hot chocolate to warm up."

They headed into the lodge and sat down at a table.

"We'll have three hot chocolates, please," said Mookie.

"Sorry," said the waitress. "We ran out of milk. Our order will be in for lunch."

"Oh, no!" cried Chuga. "I really wanted hot chocolate."

"Me, too," said Mookie, pouting.

"I can bring you some hot cider," said the waitress.
"We have plenty of that."

"Hot cider?" said Chuga.

"I never tried hot cider," said Mookie. "We'll just come back later."

"Wait," cried Traveling Bear. "I bet the cider is really good. Let's think positively and try some!"

The waitress brought three steaming cups of cider to Traveling Bear's table.

"It's yummy!" cried Chuga.

"Mmm," said Mookie.

"It's even better than hot chocolate," said Traveling Bear, licking his lips.

Soon it was time to ski again.

"I just know the lift will work perfectly," said Chuga, nodding his head.

"I just know we're going to have a great run down the mountain," said Mookie, smiling.

"I just know that by the time we get back to the lodge, there will be plenty of delicious hot chocolate to drink!" said Traveling Bear.

"Wow!" said Chuga. "That's what I call positive thinking!"

"Wow! What a day . . .

We all know that if you want good things in life to happen to you,

Here's what you need to do... 1, 2, 1 - 2 - 3

Get out of bed I said, get fed, have bread, just find a way to get there.

Travel to school on a mule, on a bike, take a hike, just find a way to get there.

Let out a moan, sing a tone, talk on the phone, just find a way to get there.

On a boat, on a goat, on a plane or on the train, just find a way to get there.

Forget about your hair, so people take a stare, who cares, just find a way to get there!

Bye, everybody!

What's Most Important?

Read the paragraphs below with your child and help them circle the words in each parenthesis that best completes the sentence.

At Gold Mountain Chuga (**wanted, did not want**) to go down the beginners' slope. To convince himself, Chuga said, (**"I can do this," "I can't do this"**). While going up the ski lift, it suddenly (**stopped, rocked back and forth**). Chuga counted to (**five, ten**) to get the ski lift going. Before they skied again, Chuga wanted some (**hot chocolate, chocolate milk**). Instead of hot chocolate, the friends tried (**hot cider, apple juice**) for the (**first, fourth**) time. Positive thinking really (**worked, didn't work**) for Traveling Bear and his friends.